The Piano Playlist

50 Popular Classics in Easy Arrangements

Arranged by
Barrie Carson Turner

ED 13860
ISMN 979-0-2201-3697-9
ISBN 978-1-84761-419-3

www.schott-music.com

Mainz · London · Madrid · Berlin · New York · Paris · Prague · Tokyo · Toronto
© 2016 SCHOTT MUSIC Ltd, London · Printed in Germany

ED 13860
British Library Cataloguing-in-Publication Data.
A catalogue record for this book is available from the British Library
ISMN 979-0-2201-3697-9
ISBN 978-1-84761-419-3

Cover design by www.josellopis.com
Prelim design and typesetting by www.adamhaystudio.com
Music setting and page layout by Scott Barnard (www.musicpreparation.co.uk)
Printed in the UK S&Co. 9299

Contents

1. Adagietto
from Symphony No.5

Gustav Mahler (1860-1911)
Arr. Barrie Carson Turner

Sehr langsam

a tempo

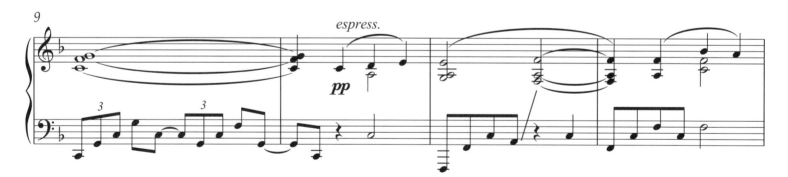

2. Air
from Suite No.3, BWV 1068

Johann Sebastian Bach (1685-1750)
Arr. Barrie Carson Turner

3. Andante
from Piano Concerto No.23, K488

Wolfgang Amadeus Mozart (1756-1791)
Arr. Barrie Carson Turner

D.S. al Coda

Coda

4. The Blue Danube

Johann Strauss II (1825-1899)
Arr. Barrie Carson Turner

Tempo di valse

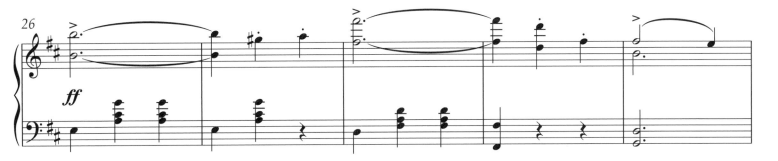

5. Canon

Johann Pachelbel (1653-1706)
Arr. Barrie Carson Turner

6. Clair de Lune
from *Suite Bergamasque*

Claude Debussy (1862-1918)
Arr. Barrie Carson Turner

7. Chanson de Matin

Edward Elgar (1857-1934)
Arr. Barrie Carson Turner

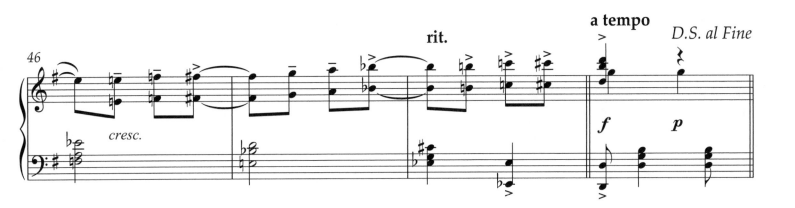

8. Chorus of the Hebrew Slaves
from *Nabucco*

Giuseppe Verdi (1813-1901)
Arr. Barrie Carson Turner

9. The Dance of the Little Swans
from *Swan Lake*

Pyotr Ilyich Tchaikovsky (1840-1893)
Arr. Barrie Carson Turner

Allegro moderato

10. Dance of the Blessèd Spirits

from *Orpheus and Eurydice*

Christoph Willibald Gluck (1714-1787)
Arr. Barrie Carson Turner

11. Danse Macabre

Camille Saint-Saëns (1835-1921)
Arr. Barrie Carson Turner

Mouvement modere de valse

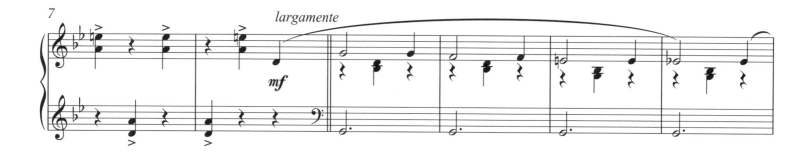

12. The Pearl Fishers' Duet

from *Les pêcheurs de perles*

George Bizet (1838-1875)
Arr. Barrie Carson Turner

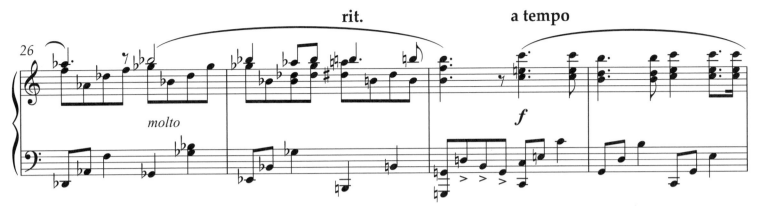

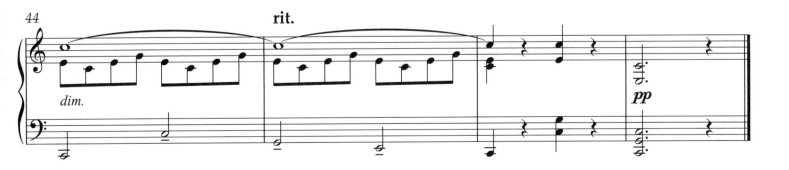

13. Emperor Concerto
2nd Movement

Ludwig van Beethoven (1770-1827)
Arr. Barrie Carson Turner

14. Flower Duet
from *Lakmé*

Léo Delibes (1836-1891)
Arr. Barrie Carson Turner

Andantino con moto

15. Gavotte
from *Holberg Suite*

Edvard Grieg (1843-1907)
Arr. Barrie Carson Turner

16. Gymnopédie No.1

Erik Satie (1866-1925)
Arr. Barrie Carson Turner

17. Habanera
from *Carmen*

George Bizet (1838-1875)
Arr. Barrie Carson Turner

Allegretto quasi andantino

18. Hallelujah Chorus
from *Messiah*

George Frideric Handel (1685-1759)
Arr. Barrie Carson Turner

Allegro

19. Hornpipe
from *Water Music*

George Frideric Handel (1685-1759)
Arr. Barrie Carson Turner

Allegro

20. Impromptu
Op.90, No. 3

Franz Schubert (1797-1828)
Arr. Barrie Carson Turner

21. Intermezzo

from *Cavalleria rusticana*

Pietro Mascagni (1863-1945)
Arr. Barrie Carson Turner

Andante sostenuto

22. Jerusalem

Hubert Parry (1848-1918)
Arr. Barrie Carson Turner

Largo, animato

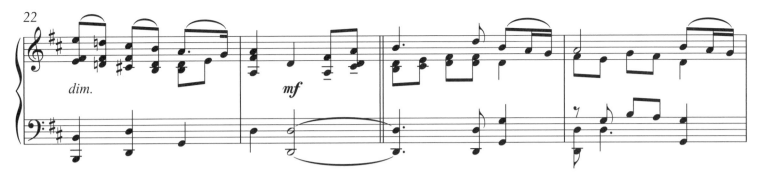

23. Jupiter
from *The Planets*

Gustav Holst (1874-1934)
Arr. Barrie Carson Turner

Andante maestoso

24. Intermezzo
from *Karelia Suite*

Jean Sibelius (1865-1957)
Arr. Barrie Carson Turner

25. Liebestraüme No.3

Franz Liszt (1811-1886)
Arr. Barrie Carson Turner

Poco allegro, con affetto

dolce cantando

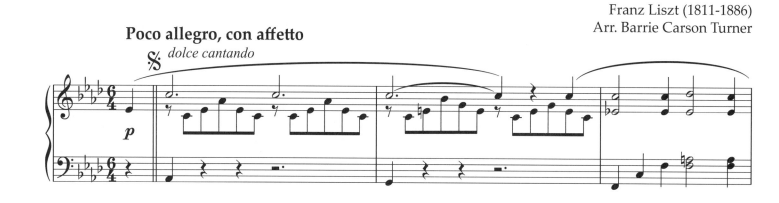

To Coda

mf

poco cresc. ed agitato

26. Menuet
from *Sonatine*

Maurice Ravel (1875-1937)
Arr. Barrie Carson Turner

Mouvement de menuet

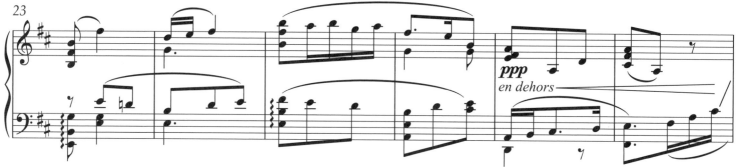

rall. _ _ _ _ _ _ _ _ _ _ _ _ _ _ _ **Plus lent**

Reprenez peu à peu le mouvt.

a tempo   **sans ralentir**

rall.

27. Menuetto
from Symphony No.104 (London)

Joseph Haydn (1732-1809)
Arr. Barrie Carson Turner

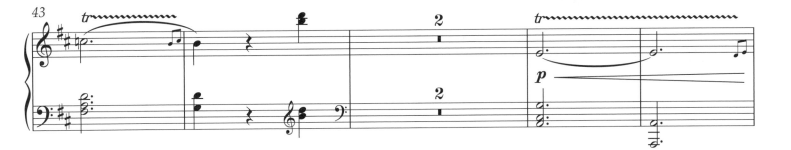

28. Méditation
from *Thaïs*

Jules Massenet (1842-1912)
Arr. Barrie Carson Turner

Andante religioso

D.S. al Coda

29. Morning
from *Peer Gynt*

Edvard Grieg (1843-1907)
Arr. Barrie Carson Turner

Allegretto pastorale

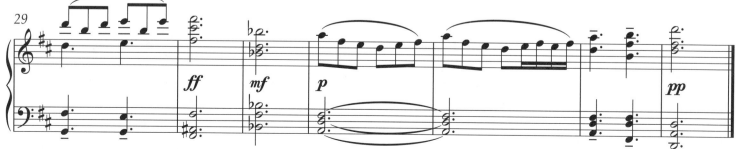

© 2016 Schott Music Ltd, London

30. Ode to Joy
from Symphony No.9

Ludwig van Beethoven (1770-1827)
Arr. Barrie Carson Turner

Allegro assai

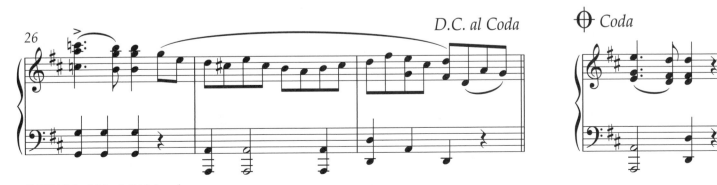

31. Nessun Dorma

from *Turandot*

Giacomo Puccini (1858-1924)
Arr. Barrie Carson Turner

Andante sostenuto

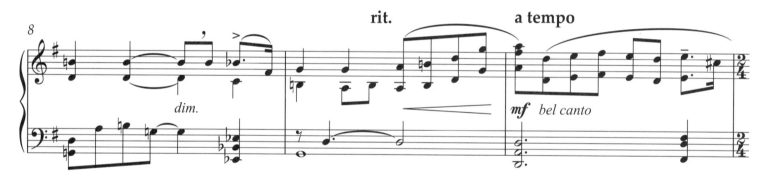

32. Nimrod
from *Enigma* Variations

Edward Elgar (1857-1934)
Arr. Barrie Carson Turner

33. Nocturne
Op. 9, No. 2

Frédéric Chopin (1810-1849)
Arr. Barrie Carson Turner

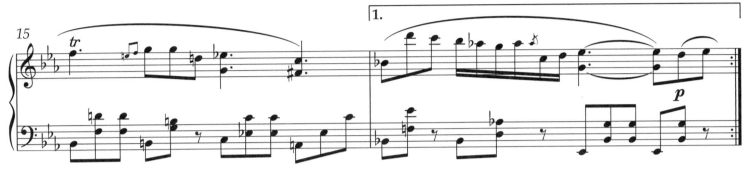

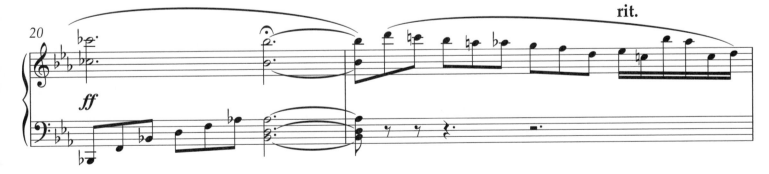

34. Non più andrai
from *The Marriage of Figaro*

Wolfgang Amadeus Mozart (1756-1791)
Arr. Barrie Carson Turner

D.S. al Fine

35. O Mio Babbino Caro
from *Gianni Schicchi*

Giacomo Puccini (1858-1924)
Arr. Barrie Carson Turner

36. Dance of the Sugar Plum Fairy
from *The Nutcracker*

Pyotr Ilyich Tchaikovsky (1840-1893)
Arr. Barrie Carson Turner

Andante ma non troppo

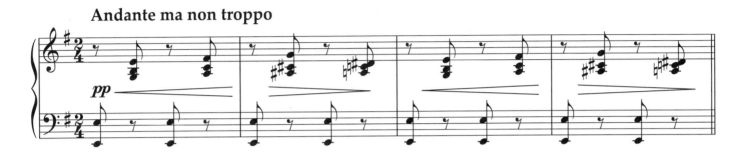

37. Prélude à l'après-midi d'un faune

Claude Debussy (1862-1918)
Arr. Barrie Carson Turner

38. Ride of the Valkyries
from *Die Walküre*

Richard Wagner (1813-1883)
Arr. Barrie Carson Turner

To Coda ⊕

D.S. al Coda

⊕ Coda

39. Spring
from *The Four Seasons*

Antonio Vivaldi (1678-1741)
Arr. Barrie Carson Turner

40. Symphony No.1
4th movement

Johannes Brahms (1833-1897)
Arr. Barrie Carson Turner

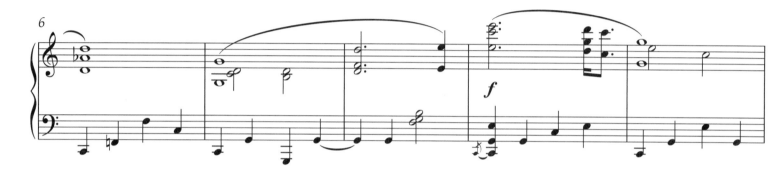

Allegro non troppo, ma con brio

41. The Old Castle
from *Pictures at an Exhibition*

Modest Mussorgsky (1839-1881)
Arr. Barrie Carson Turner

42. The Swan
from *The Carnival of the Animals*

Camille Saint-Saëns (1835-1921)
Arr. Barrie Carson Turner

Andantino grazioso

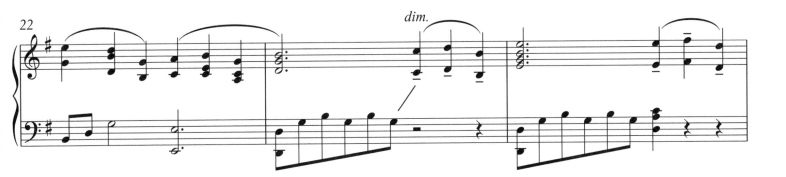

43. The Trout

Franz Schubert (1797-1828)
Arr. Barrie Carson Turner

44. Traumerei
from *Scenes from Childhood*, Op. 15

Robert Schumann (1810-1856)
Arr. Barrie Carson Turner

45. Toreador Song
from *Carmen*

George Bizet (1838-1875)
Arr. Barrie Carson Turner

Allegro moderato

46. Violin Concerto

Felix Mendelssohn Bartholdy (1809-1847)
Arr. Barrie Carson Turner

47. Vltava
from *Má Vlast*

Bedřich Smetana (1824-1884)
Arr. Barrie Carson Turner

Allegro commodo non agitato

48. Waltz
from *Coppélia*

Léo Delibes (1836-1891)
Arr. Barrie Carson Turner

49. When I Am Laid in Earth
from *Dido and Aeneas*

Henry Purcell (1659-1695)
Arr. Barrie Carson Turner

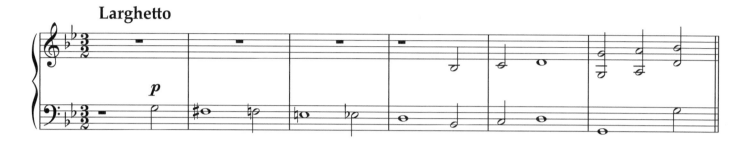

50. Waltz
Op. 39, No. 15

Johannes Brahms (1833-1897)
Arr. Barrie Carson Turner

Teneramente e grazioso

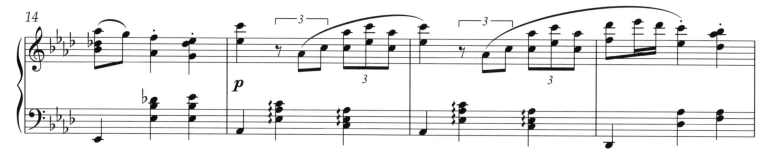

poco rit.

RELAX
WITH
YOUR PIANO

- Unwind and enjoy some 'me time' with these new collections for piano

- Well-known pieces and rare gems, selected for their relaxing qualities

- Easy to intermediate difficulty level

Relax with Classical Piano
ED 13850

Relax with Baroque Piano
ED 13849

Relax with Folk Piano
ED 13852

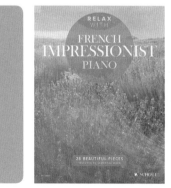

Relax with French Impressionist Piano
ED 13853

Relax with Romantic Piano
ED 13851

SCHOTT
www.schott-music.com